THIS BOOK BELONGS TO

Practicing for Heaven

To Maxine Cameron,

a wonderful pianist and an even better example

—BW and WWR

For Ralph and Leon, who taught me and put me

on the path of becoming an artist.

—BC

Library of Congress Cataloging-in-Publication Data

Wilcox, Brad, author.
  Practicing for heaven : the parable of the piano lessons / Brad Wilcox.
    pages cm
  Includes bibliographical references.
    ISBN 978-1-60907-997-0 (hardbound : alk. paper) 1. Atonement—The Church of Jesus Christ of Latter-day Saints. 2. Piano—Instruction and study.
I. Rosborough, Wendee Wilcox, author. II. Call, Brian D., illustrator. III. Title.
  BX8643.A85W565 2015
  242—dc23   2014031430

Printed in China   11/2014
R. R. Donnelley, Shenzhen, China

10 9 8 7 6 5 4 3 2 1

Practicing for Heaven

THE PARABLE OF THE PIANO LESSONS

BRAD WILCOX

WENDEE WILCOX ROSBOROUGH

Illustrated by BRIAN CALL

DESERET
BOOK

SALT LAKE CITY, UTAH

David stared at the piano. His limp fingers rested on the keys, but they made no sound.

Mom called from the kitchen, "I want to hear some practicing in there!"

"Why do I have to practice? *Anything* would be better than this!" David moaned.

"Even cleaning the bathroom?" Mom said, smiling, as she popped her head around the corner.

"Maybe," David mumbled, frowning.

Mom entered the room and put her arm around her son's shoulders. "I've already paid Mrs. Lundell, and I don't want to see you waste this opportunity."

"But it's hard," David complained.

"I know," Mom said. "It was hard when I learned how to play, too. But this is what you wanted, remember? You wanted to learn to play the piano like your friend Ethan."

David looked up at his mother and said, "But Mom, I'm just not very good. I keep hitting the wrong notes. It takes me *forever* to get it right. I don't know if I'll ever play like Ethan."

Mom sighed. "Anyone who wants to play well has to practice. Just keep practicing and I promise you'll get better."

"But I don't even *care* about getting better. There are lots of other people in the world who don't play the piano!"

"That's true," Mom said. "But this isn't just about playing the piano. It's a lot bigger than that."

David looked at his mom, puzzled.

Mom motioned for him to scoot over on the bench so she could sit. "During the next few years, there might be times when you want to give up on things that are much more important than the piano. You'll need strength to keep going, and that's when you'll need to turn to Him." Mom pointed to a picture of Jesus hanging on the wall.

David still looked confused. "What does practicing the piano have to do with Jesus?"

Mom chuckled and asked, "Who paid for your piano lessons?"

"You did," David said.

"And because I paid for your lessons, I can ask you to practice, right?"

David nodded.

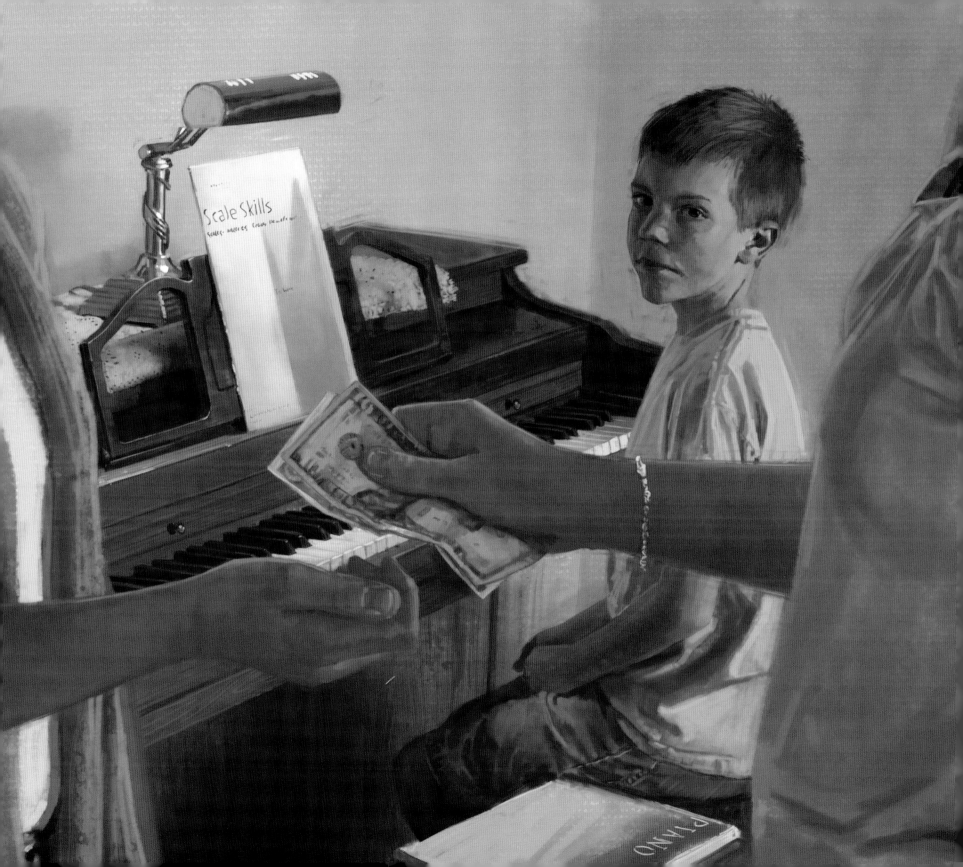

"Well, Jesus paid the ultimate price for our sins and mistakes, so He can ask something of us. He asks us to follow Him and keep His commandments—not to pay Him back, but to help us become more like Him."

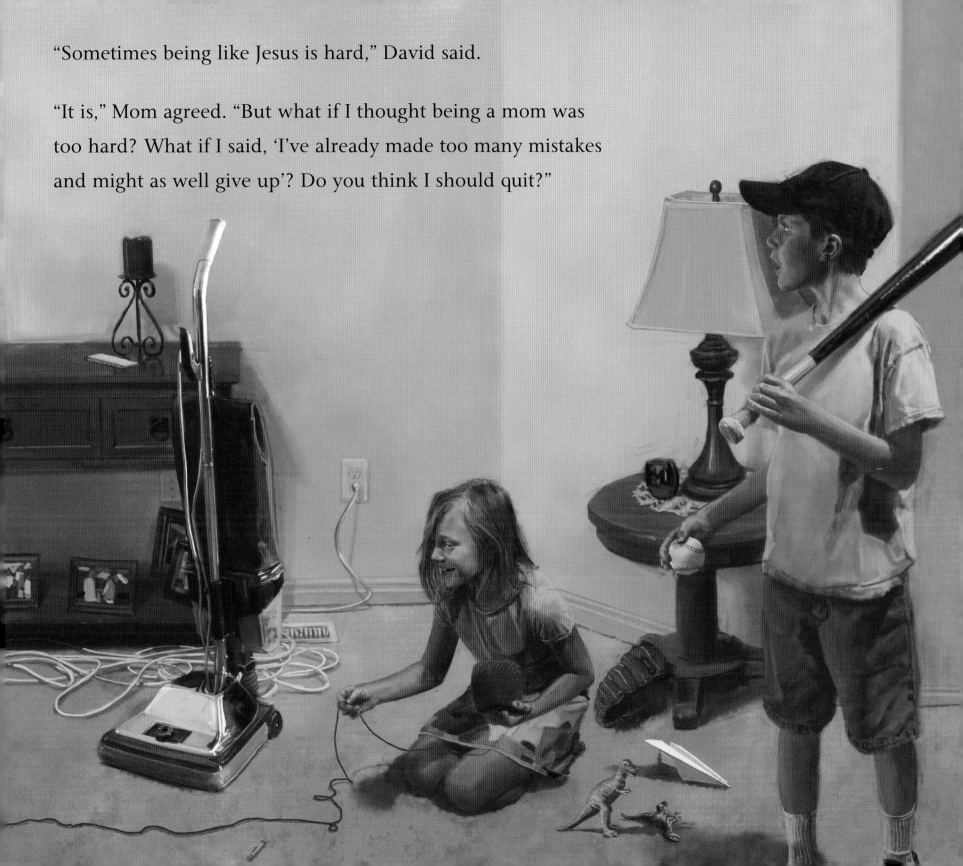

"Sometimes being like Jesus is hard," David said.

"It is," Mom agreed. "But what if I thought being a mom was too hard? What if I said, 'I've already made too many mistakes and might as well give up'? Do you think I should quit?"

David looked surprised and said, "No. You can't quit!"

"You're right," Mom said. "I don't need to be perfect; I just have to keep trying." She looked up at the picture and continued, "And that's what Jesus might say when we feel discouraged. By following Christ we aren't earning our way to heaven. We are learning to become the kind of people who want to live there someday."

"We're *practicing* for heaven," David realized.

"Exactly!" Mom laughed as she gave her son a sideways squeeze. "And Christ will strengthen and help us no matter how long it takes."

David glanced again at the picture above the piano and back at the music in front of him. With a look of determination he took a deep breath, placed his fingers on the keys, and started playing.

As Mom listened, she thought about how far he had come since he first began and smiled. David was learning a lot about piano and, more important, about life.

Teaching about the Atonement

Teaching children about the Atonement can be challenging; however, there are a few principles that will make a difference:

Seek natural teaching moments. Along with formal lessons and talks, look for everyday opportunities. In this story, the mom found a teaching moment when her son was discouraged about practicing the piano. You can find similar moments when a pet dies, when a child makes a mistake, when someone you know is facing a challenge, or when a child is striving to reach a worthy goal.

Ask questions. In this story the mom responded to her son's question with another question. Doing so is not an attempt to avoid answering, but an opportunity to find out what the child knows and to help him or her discover answers on his or her own.

Share personal experiences. Think about when the Atonement first became meaningful to you. When have you received a special manifestation of grace? Explain the details of such experiences. Along with saying, "I know Jesus lives and loves us," express how you came to this knowledge. Children respond well to these stories.

Include multiple aspects of the Atonement. Children need to understand that Christ's gifts to us are many. For example, explain that Jesus' Atonement offers us life after death and sin (1 Corinthians 15:22; Isaiah 1:18), but also life amid trials and challenges (Alma 7:11–12). Beyond this, it offers us the opportunity to be transformed (John 10:10). Not only can we return home to God, but we can become more like Him (Matthew 5:48).

Focus on the child. Among the letters in the word *atonement* is the word *me*. The Atonement becomes truly meaningful when it is personalized. Although God has many children, He is a perfect parent who cares for each individually. The Atonement was performed for all mankind, but also for each individual. It is up to each of us to appreciate, accept, apply, and internalize it.

Provide purpose for the suffering. To accomplish the Atonement, Christ selflessly and lovingly offered His life and endured spiritual anguish that was beyond the capacity of any mortal. Dwelling on Christ's death and suffering can sometimes be overwhelming and disturbing for children. Emphasize the purpose for Christ's suffering: to make possible the plan of redemption, to preserve our freedom, to offer us the chance to live eternally with loved ones, to give us the opportunity to change and be better, to offer us peace, hope, and relief. We can help children discover all that is possible because of Christ's suffering and, when the time is right, see purpose in their own difficult challenges as well.

Use visuals and simple language. This story was written in the hope of making a difficult concept more accessible for children. You'll notice the mom pointed to a picture of the Savior. We can do the same. Instead of using the word *grace*, the mom spoke of how Christ can strengthen and help us. We can follow a similar pattern. Call the Atonement a priceless gift. *Redemption* can be related to improvement. *Resurrection* is living after we die. *Eternal life* is the opportunity to live with God and family. *Exaltation* is reaching our highest potential, and *repentance* is changing and being better. As children get older, they can be taught the specific doctrinal words to go with the concepts they've already learned.

Recognize progress. Perfection may be our ultimate goal, but for now we can be content with progress in the right direction. Just like playing the piano, growth and development take time. Learning takes time. Help children learn grace by assuring them that God is long-suffering, that change is a process, and that repentance is a pattern in our lives. Help them see how they can try again when they make mistakes. Teach that the blessings of Christ's Atonement are continuous and His strength is made perfect in our weakness (see 2 Corinthians 12:9). We can all, as it says in the Doctrine and Covenants, "continue in patience until [we] are perfected" (D&C 67:13).

Use additional resources. Look up the word *grace* in the Bible Dictionary and review the definition given there. *True to the Faith* and *Preach My Gospel* also include clear definitions of the Atonement and related topics written with simple language that children can understand. General conference talks by the leaders of the Church can be used as guides as you learn and teach about the Atonement.

SELECTED GENERAL CONFERENCE TALKS

David A. Bednar, "Clean Hands and a Pure Heart," *Ensign*, November 2007, 80–83.

Linda K. Burton, "Is Faith in the Atonement of Jesus Christ Written in Our Hearts?" *Ensign*, November 2012, 111–15.

D. Todd Christofferson, "The Divine Gift of Repentance," *Ensign*, November 2011, 38–41.

Bruce C. Hafen, "The Atonement: All for All," *Ensign*, May 2004, 97–99.

Jeffrey R. Holland, "The Laborers in the Vineyard," *Ensign*, May 2012, 31–33.

Richard G. Scott, "Personal Strength through the Atonement of Jesus Christ," *Ensign*, November 2013, 82–84.

ADDITIONAL RESOURCES BY BRAD WILCOX

"His Grace Is Sufficient," Brigham Young University devotional address, 12 July 2011; available at http://speeches.byu.edu/?act=viewitem&id=1966; accessed 15 July 2014; see also "His Grace Is Sufficient," *Ensign*, September 2013, 35–37, and "His Grace Is Sufficient," *New Era*, August 2012, 12–15.

The Continuous Atonement (Salt Lake City: Deseret Book, 2009), *The Continuous Conversion* (Salt Lake City: Deseret Book, 2013), and *The Continuous Atonement for Teens* (Salt Lake City: Deseret Book, 2015).

Grace is not the absence of God's high
expectations, but the presence of His power.

It is help we receive from God even though we
don't deserve or earn it.

It covers our debt, changes our hearts, and
strengthens us to keep trying—no matter what.

—SEE ETHER 12:27; 2 CORINTHIANS 12:9;
DOCTRINE AND COVENANTS 17:8; 78:7